OLYMPIC

*

ECOSYSTEMS OF THE PENINSULA

PHOTOGRAPHY BY *Pat O'Hara*
TEXT BY *Michael Smithson*

AMERICAN & WORLD GEOGRAPHIC PUBLISHING

ACKNOWLEDGMENTS

*

I would like to gratefully acknowledge the assistance of the following individuals for their input or review of the manuscript: Paul Crawford, Paul Gleeson, Mike Gurling, Cat Hoffman, Doug Houston, John Meyer, Bruce Moorhead, Ed Schreiner, Susan Schultz, Hank Warren, Jacilee Wray, Olympic National Park; Nelsa Buckingham, Olympic Peninsula botanist; John Calambokidas, Cascadia Research Institute; Steve Jeffries, Washington Department of Wildlife; James Lichatowich, fisheries biologist; Paul Ringgold, Olympic Natural Resource Center; Tom Sayer, U.S. Forest Service; Fred Sharpe, Olympic Peninsula Naturalist; Kathleen Snow, USFS/Olympic Natural Resource Center; Dick Stewart, University of Washington. Finally, my deep appreciation to Liz, Kate, and Ben Smithson for their love and support.

—M.S.

Many thanks to Tina Smith-O'Hara and Heidi Lunt for overseeing the rapid succession of events in meeting the deadlines for this publication. I am also grateful for the companionship of all my hiking and traveling partners who enjoyed the real-life experiences that this book's photos represent. Barbara Fifer, Publications Manager of American & World Geographic, deserves much credit for guiding this book through the production process in record time in concert with Linda McCray, the graphic designer, and the authors.

—P.O.

Library of Congress Cataloging-in-Publication Data

O'Hara, Pat, 1947-
Olympic : ecosystems of the peninsula / photography by Pat O'Hara ; text by Michael Smithson.
  p. cm.
ISBN 1-56037-042-4
1. Ecology—Washington (State)—Olympic Peninsula. 2. Biotic communities—Washington (State)—Olympic Peninsula. 3. Olympic Peninsula (Wash.) 4. Ecology—Washington (State)—Olympic Peninsula—Pictorial works. 5. Biotic communities—Washington (State)—Olympic Peninsula—Pictorial works. 6. Olympic Peninsula (Wash.)—Pictorial works. I. Smithson, Michael T. II. Title.
QH105.W202 1993
574.5 ' 09797 ' 94--dc20

93-10420

Above: *Old-growth forest in the Sol Duc River Valley.*
Title page: *Sunrise view of the Strait of Juan de Fuca, Protection Island, and Mt. Baker, looking across the peninsula's dry rainshadow country.*

———— ✳ ————

Front cover: *First light graces pink mountain heather and White Mountain at the headwaters divide of the Quinault and Dosewallips rivers.*
Back cover: *The Olympic Peninsula from space.*
© *Advanced Satellite Productions Inc. 1993*

CONTENTS

———— ✳ ————

FOREWORD

✳

*F*rom Sentinel Peak, Karl Wegmann and I enjoyed the impressive views of the surrounding Olympic Mountains. To the east, Thousand Acre Meadow spread out below us, the Dosewallips River Valley, Mt. Constance and Lost Peak were distinct features. Mt. Anderson and the Eel Glacier, the hydrologic center of the Olympic Peninsula, dominated the landscape just to the south. The deeply cut and heavily forested Elwha River Valley separated us from the maritime-influenced western peaks. This wilderness panorama was stunning as it radiated from our viewpoint. Evening sidelighting washed the west-facing ridgeline on Sentinel Peak and Mt. Anderson. I photographed as the landscape came alive with the warm tones of low-angle lighting and elongated shadows. Fulfilled with the day's activities, we began our descent after sunset to our camp in Dose Meadow.

The next morning and early afternoon were occupied meandering through and exploring Thousand Acre Meadow in the July heat wave. Several bears foraged in the heather patches throughout the meadow. We stopped to photograph their behavior on our way to the ridge above Silt Creek. After lunch we fell asleep among the boulders.

Thousand Acre Meadow was moderately dry and most of the wildflowers had passed their prime so we decided to return to Dose Meadow and gain access to Lost Pass trail for late afternoon and evening photography. Earlier we had talked with some acquaintances who told us that the Lost Pass area was in full bloom.

It was a steep ascent to Lost Pass. I stopped often in the shade, dripping with perspiration, while Karl bounded effortlessly up the trail with the energy of a black-tail deer yearling. He waited patiently for me at the pass. As I crested the ridge an elegant alpine wildflower meadow opened in front of me! Like Dose Meadow we had it all to ourselves! Karl decided to scramble to the top of Lost Peak while I scouted the area for potential photo compositions. The pace was slow, the surroundings gorgeous and the temperature a bit cooler. Heather, daisies, Indian paintbrush, and avalanche lilies were abundant. Karl returned just about the time that the quality of light was favorable for serious photography. At first we worked the lilies and paintbrush that were wind-sheltered in the lee of the main ridge. The sun lowered toward the horizon as we moved to a place overlooking the Lost River Valley. Clouds began to gather around the sun, and then a strange and unexpected

Upper Royal Basin and the Needles Peaks on the northeastern flank of Olympic National Park.

light emanated from them. This mystical illumination was brief and we watched curiously for several minutes before the clouds parted a bit.

Solar eclipses are rare in our short lifespans. I had had the rarer occurrence of standing with a friend on a beautiful wilderness ridge surrounded by solitude during one of these natural events. It reinforced my appreciation of the intrinsic beauty of nature and the life-nurturing energy of the sun.

I fondly remember a hike to Shi Shi Beach in Olympic National Park when Tina and I took our four-month-old daughter, Trisha, on her first backpacking trip. We planned the trip to coincide with a full moon for photography potential and for a symbolic introduction to the Coast for Trisha. Our friends Kate and John accompanied us with their four-and-a-half-month-old son, Duncan.

Our experimental trip met with typical Washington maritime weather. Clouds persisted throughout the afternoon as we hiked over Shi Shi Beach. Trisha was settled into a baby pack on the front of Tina. We stopped a few times for scenic interludes while our friends continued to the campsite. Tina rested against some driftwood while Trisha alternately nursed and paused in response to the sounds of the coastal environment. The salt air was refreshing and it was great to be outdoors.

That night the full moon was blocked by a curtain of overcast, and darkness enveloped our campsite among the huge Sitka spruce trees. But to our young voyagers, this didn't seem to make much difference. They were content on their first wilderness sojourn.

Above: Club moss ornaments a vine maple in the Hoh Rain Forest.

— * —

Facing page: Both trumpeter swans (seen here) and tundra swans spend winters on the peninsula.

The following morning we arose to the sounds of seagulls dancing along the surf. The scene was monochrome. After a leisurely morning start, I decided to take a father-and-daughter walk from the campsite in the light mist to the seastacks at the Point of the Arches. With Trisha bundled up and perched on my shoulders, we worked our way south on the soft sand, stopping often to take in the wilderness coastline. I could feel her body flexing as she turned in every direction, filling her senses. The crows flew above, harassing the gulls. Large evergreen trees bordered the beach and many designs were evident in the sand. At the Point of the Arches we looked at the rock sculptures jutting out of the tideline. Our walk to the point and back to camp was defined by a sinuous line of footsteps on the beach, which corresponded with our path of curiosity.

We finished our round trip by sitting on the driftwood adjacent to the campsite.

After this active exploration, Trisha sat quietly in my lap, her eyes intent on the shorebirds. John and Duncan sat beside us with the same silence and curiosity.

Curiosity is an infant's virtue. Wide-eyed and alert, Trisha and Duncan absorbed more from the wilderness experience than we will probably ever realize. Positive experiences such as this, early in a child's life, can only enrich the process of human development. I'd say that we had gotten off to a good start as a family.

I did photograph on our return hike to the trailhead. These images will always have a special meaning to me because they are associated with the first wilderness experiences we had with Trisha. Our greatest satisfaction with this short introductory backpacking trip was watching Trisha and Duncan marvel at the world in front of them…a world of wonder and hope.

From the saltwater coastline, to the temperate west-side rain forest and the peninsula's green skirt of mixed evergreen forests, to the alpine meadows and glaciers of the high country, the greater Olympic ecosystem exhibits some of the most impressive natural diversity on the planet. The centerpiece, Olympic National Park, is recognized by UNESCO as a World Biosphere Reserve and World Heritage Site. Both designations recognize the park as an important world resource. Beyond the boundaries of the national park are other vital land management units that contribute to keeping the greater ecosystem intact. National wildlife refuges, state, county and local natural resource areas and dedicated wilderness areas managed by the U.S. Forest Service are some important examples. In addition, many of the peninsula's rivers are proposed for federal wild and scenic designation. All contribute to the greater ecosystem's integrity.

I'm fortunate to be living on the Olympic Peninsula and to have been influenced by this greater ecosystem. Though my travels take me out of state to photograph I always look forward to returning home to my family and the environment I've come to love.

Michael Smithson and I have endeavored to give you a cross-section introduction to this very diverse, complex and intricate region of the world. Of course, it is impossible to be all-inclusive in this brief publication. We hope you will be inspired to take the next personal step to learn, in depth, more about the beautiful ecological interrelationships that make the Olympic Peninsula a living museum.

Pat O'Hara
Mount Pleasant, 1993

*T*he quiet waters of Puget Sound were barely discernible in the dark

lowlands, over a mile below. In the pre-dawn air, tiny lights flickered from

the distant cities. From this mountaintop perch in the east Olympics, the

entire Puget lowlands spread before me. I was nestled in my sleeping bag

just a few feet below the peak's summit, waiting for the sun's rays to wash

over the rock. But I was not alone.

The words of Chief Seattle came to mind. In giving his land away over a

century ago, he said when we think we are alone, in city or forest, we will

not be. His people's spirits would remain. Those who "once filled and still

love this beautiful land."

The millions of people below were beginning to wake. For most, the natural

world was somewhere else, separate from the realm of everyday existence.

How many of us know just how dependent we are on the land and water

that surroundsus? Who has not felt the peace that comes from just sitting

in the woods?

A curious marten bounded up the rocks and stopped a few feet away. We

stared for a moment into each other's eyes. Satisfied I was neither food nor

threat, it moved on—leaving me with a glimpse into the wild heart

of this land.

OLYMPIC PENINSULA

——————————— ✳ ———————————

*F*rom Seattle's gray skyscrapers, the Olympic Mountains look like an emerald isle. Shimmering between water and sky, the snow-covered peaks, primeval forests and miles of untamed beaches speak of adventure, beauty and solitude. A remarkable diversity of wildlife lives here—puffins and murres raise their chicks above the crashing surf, while cougars and golden eagles hunt in alpine meadows a few miles inland.

The Olympic Peninsula is an intricate puzzle of different habitats, each with its own flora and fauna. Like the cells of a single organism, these habitats may appear to function independently of each other, but their health depends on the vitality of the entire ecosystem.

This is a land of contrast. Humans have harvested the peninsula's abundant resources since hunters tracked mastodon and bison through soggy lowlands some 12,000 years ago. Today, these natural riches provide jobs and economic rewards, but not without consequence. Our western culture has long held the belief that nature was ours to subordinate. With our increasing technological prowess, we can systematically overharvest animals and plants until they are "endangered" or eliminated from an area.

Our appetite for resources is evident in the thousands of square miles of clear-cut forest that surround the peninsula's wilderness. Now only a fraction of the ancient forests remain.

By the beginning of the century, Roosevelt elk, fur seals and gray whales had been nearly hunted to extinction while wolves and sea otter were completely eliminated from the peninsula. Spotted owls and marbled murrelets are currently threatened with extinction, along with several other animals and a number of salmon stocks. A hundred years ago, salmon returned from the ocean in numbers so great settlers could harvest them with pitchforks. Today, low populations force severe fishing restrictions.

Various government agencies and companies have conflicting priorities for managing these resources. Despite a mosaic of political boundaries, the greater ecosystem of the peninsula stretches from the mountaintops to the coast and beyond. It is a system unto itself—what happens in one area affects another. Rivers provide a vital link between the ocean and the mountains—salmon bring rich nutrients from the sea to the land. Marbled murrelets carry small fish from the ocean as far as

50 miles inland to feed their hungry chicks. Thousands of elk migrate from lowlands to high meadows.

Land owners are beginning to realize that the peninsula's ecosystem extends beyond their individual boundaries. Some are working together to solve common problems—salmon runs on the Elwha River, which has been dammed for over 80 years, may be restored. Gray whales were brought back from the brink of extinction and the peninsula now boasts healthy populations of sea otter and Roosevelt elk. But we now face environmental problems that affect many people. These difficult issues will only be resolved when they are seen through the eyes of all who are affected.

OF MOUNTAINS AND SEA

Marymere Falls after a winter storm near Lake Crescent.

The peninsula is as unique as it is beautiful. It was literally thrust up from below the ocean and smashed onto the North American continent about 25 million years ago. Before then, the Pacific coastline was near Seattle. The mass of basalt that created the spectacular peaks seen from Puget Sound was originally part of a giant chain of undersea volcanoes and rock that formed beneath the ocean. The rocks of Mt. Olympus and most of the interior mountains were formed from the sand, mud and decaying marine organisms of the ocean floor.

To most of us, geologic forces seem a thing of the past. But each day, the churning internal forces of the earth mold and shape the earth's surface. Massive plates of crust continue to slowly rip apart or crash into each other in this grand, inexorable demolition derby.

Our continent is shoved westward a couple inches every year. If North America continues to move in this direction, our descendants may one day be able to jump from the peninsula to the island of Japan! These same forces are still lifting the relatively young Olympics—some geologists think they are the fastest rising mountains in the world.

Today the peninsula is nearly isolated from the mainland by water; in the past it has been separated many times by ice. Lobes of the immense continental glaciers, thousands of feet thick, covered what is now Puget Sound and the Strait of Juan de Fuca. Sea level was three to four hundred feet lower during these glacial periods, when more of the earth's water was locked up in ice.

Most of the peninsula was covered with alpine glaciers during these times of general cooling, but biologists believe some life survived in protected areas called

Low-tide design,
South Beach
Wilderness, Olympic
National Park.

refugia. These ice-free stretches could be found along the extended coastal plains or high in the drier mountains of the eastern Olympics.

During the thousands of years of near-isolation from the main continent, a number of plants and animals evolved into different species or subspecies. Flett's violet and the Olympic marmot are found nowhere else in the world. Researchers also believe animals like bighorn sheep, mountain goat, grizzly bear, lynx, pika, ptarmigan and several others did not cross the ice, water and lowlands that separated the Cascades and the Olympics. (If they did, their populations became extinct.)

Weather patterns on the peninsula are extremely varied. On the west side of the peninsula, the mountains block the path of storms rolling in from the ocean and wring trillions of gallons of water from the clouds each year. Parts of the rain forest receive over 160 inches of rain annually—more than twice the height of a human. But on the northeast side of the Olympic Peninsula, the drier air drops an average 17 inches of moisture each year. Here oaks grow in prairie savannas and the unwary person may sit too close to a cactus.

Natural cycles seem intensified on the peninsula. Moisture from the ocean condenses as it rises over the peaks, falls as rain or snow, and begins its wild race back to the sea. The water carries bits of the mountains that flush into the ocean, sink to the bottom where they will eventually become the building blocks of future ranges.

FOOTPRINTS ON THE LAND

Human impact on the peninsula is also evident. Archeological sites, including ancient coastal whaling villages buried under mudslides, give us clues about what life was like here thousands of years ago. Native peoples were proud, industrious, artistic and

often warlike. Their life depended on the peninsula's plants and animals—from the red cedar alone, they fashioned a vast array of artifacts including watertight cooking boxes, rope, clothing, diapers, giant sea-going canoes, and houses.

On the ocean, hunters speared seals and glided their canoes close enough to plunge harpoons into gray whales. Messengers traveled from tribe to tribe across mountain paths and people lived in summer camps among the peaks where they gathered berries and hunted elk. The peninsula's early inhabitants respected the spirits and treasures of the mountains, forest and sea.

After the first contacts with western culture a little more than two hundred years ago, half to two thirds of the indigenous people died from introduced diseases like smallpox. In the 1800s, treaties placed the tribes on reservations. Today, ten Native American tribes live on the peninsula and a number of individuals continue in their ancestors' tradition. Communities strive to preserve a heritage, language and culture that evolved over several thousand years.

Tribal members now use the modern technology and harvesting techniques that western culture introduced. Nearly all of the old-growth cedar, spruce, fir and hemlock has been cut from their lands. Hunting whales and sea mammals was restricted long ago to help preserve these animals. Tribal fish hatcheries attempt to supplant wild salmon and a number of American Indians fish from commercial boats.

Hundreds of generations of Native American use caused little impact on the Olympic Peninsula. This may have been due to comparatively small populations, different technology, and abundant food sources, but in the last 200 years people have changed the peninsula dramatically. If we look close, it's easy to see the impacts of our consumptive lifestyles.

Trees are now cut by the millions to be transformed into lumber, plywood, shakes for roofs, yellow-page directories and other items like disposable diapers and ice cream filler. In the last twenty years, high prices and limited regulations encouraged companies to harvest trees faster than they could regrow.

The waters surrounding the peninsula are crowded with oil tankers, container ships, submarines, fishing vessels, pleasure boats, ferries and barges. The resources have provided jobs and economic growth, but what will the peninsula look like two hundred years from now? Will cities the size of Seattle sprawl across the lowlands? Will high-rise condos border the wilderness?

The peninsula's beauty and diversity should remind people that we too are a part of this magnificent ecosystem, not just casual visitors. Even in our recreation, we need to be thoughtful. Millions of people impact vegetation, trails, wildlife and solitude—the very things we come to enjoy.

The future of this land depends on the decisions each of us makes today. If we work together we can find ways to continue to reap the treasures of the peninsula and preserve its beauty for our children. This "emerald isle" can be a place where resources are harvested in an environmentally safe and sustainable manner; a place where we come to rest; and a place where wildlife and natural processes flourish.

Above: Olympic chipmunk in the mountains' high country.

——————— ✳ ———————

Facing page: Big-leaf maple leaves along the Dosewallips River, Olympic National Forest.

The moon reflects from a thousand small pools of water caught in the rocks of the receding tide. Iridescent waves wash gently upon the shore and the silence of the night surrounds me. The occasional cry of a seabird skips across the water like a stone. Earlier in the day, gray whales danced their slow, rhythmic ballets offshore while sea otters and seals played among the kelp forests. This was true wilderness—rugged coastline and sandy beaches stretched in either direction as far as I could see. Something touched me deep inside and stirred hidden ancestral memories.

Humans lived like this for millions of years. Our headlong flight into computers and cappuccinos has been a recent one—returning to the wilderness does the heart tremendous good.

THE COAST

✳

Water defines and sustains the Olympic Peninsula. Bounded by the Pacific Ocean, the Strait of Juan de Fuca and Puget Sound, the land is married to the sea.

Far off the coast, albatross skim across the wave tops, while an occasional blue whale glides through the gray water. This rare giant, the largest living animal, was hunted until less than one percent of its former population remained. Several other species of whales sporadically swim past the peninsula, including the sperm whale of *Moby Dick* fame.

Closer to shore, thousands of gray whales migrate near the beaches each spring and fall. Some now spend the summer off Olympic's headlands, straining food from the kelp forests or rooting along the seafloor in search of invertebrates. They bring enormous quantities of water and mud into their mouths, then force it back out through comb-like plates of baleen that hang from their upper jaw. The baleen strains out the thousands of pounds of minute animals whales eat each day.

Coastal Indians from the Northwest tip of the peninsula hunted gray, minke, humpback and even blue whales for centuries. The hunts were steeped in ritual—it is said the wife of the chief would lie still in her longhouse bed during the quest to ensure the whale's cooperation. Harpoon tips were lashed to sealskin floats that kept the whale near the surface and eventually exhausted the wounded animal. After a whale was dispatched with a lance, a diver sewed its mouth shut to keep it from sinking as it was towed to shore.

By the time a whaling station was established in Grays Harbor in the early 1900s, the gray whale was nearly extinct. The whalers referred to these animals as "devilfish" due to the female's fierce tendency to defend her young. Now protected for several decades, the population has risen to more than 21,000 and the species recently was removed from the endangered species list.

Each spring, gray whales tend to migrate along the coast in or near kelp beds, possibly to protect calves from predators such as great white sharks or orcas. Like wolves, orcas—or killer—whales, often hunt in packs and will attack large whales, but they most often feed on smaller prey. Different pods will specialize in feeding on salmon, squid, or mammals like harbor seals, although they will eat whatever is available. A number of theories exist about the orca's prominent dorsal fin. It may help regulate temperature, be a secondary sexual characteristic, or act as a keel to help the whale carve tight arcs through the water.

The waters off the coast teem with a variety of life. In summer, currents combine with wind and earth's rotation to drive surface waters away from the shore. As the colder, nutrient-rich waters from rock sea floors "upwell" to replace them, they fertilize the microscopic plants living just beneath the surface. These plants, or phytoplankton, are the first link of a vast food chain that includes humans. Phytoplankton produce most of the oxygen we breathe and may play an important role in regulating precipitation and world climate.

Every few years, changes in the trade winds far out over the Pacific cause a phenomenon known as "El Niño" (little child). These changes allow warm cells of water to be trapped against the coast, disrupting the upwelling. Many plankton die in the warmer temperatures, breaking the food chain, while other poisonous microorganisms thrive. Their toxins concentrate in the bodies of filter feeders like clams to the point that people become seriously ill or die after eating them. El Niño has also been blamed for reducing rainfall, decreasing the productivity of both the ocean and the land.

UNDERWATER FORESTS

The forests of the land we are familiar with have an undersea counterpart. Kelp forests reach toward the sunlight from the rocky bottoms of the coast and inland waters. When they wash ashore, the long hollow stalks of these fascinating seaweeds remind us of whips.

Kelp grow anew each year from miniature plantlets and are the fastest growing plants in the world. In some locations they may grow as much as two feet in one day! Bull kelp averages between 20 and 80 feet in length, but one plant was found in Alaska that stretched over 270 feet. Holdfasts resembling gnarled hands anchor them to rocky seafloors, while bulbs filled with carbon monoxide gas float the blades near the water's surface.

Animals ranging from tiny invertebrates to whales use these forests of seaweed. Otters and seals weave gracefully through the strands hunting fish that hide among the blades. Kelp is eaten by spine-tipped sea urchins which, in turn, are a favorite food of the sea otter. With the reintroduction of the sea otter in 1969, urchin populations have decreased and kelp beds are beginning to increase. Kelp forests dampen wave action and cause more sand to settle on the beach. But forest clearcutting

Kelp design along the Pacific Coast.

Gulls, residents of the Olympic coast, in flight.

on land may cause excessive sediments to settle over the seafloor—eliminating kelp beds in some locations.

Unlike river otters, which also live along the coast, sea otters spend most of their life in the ocean. They wrap strands of kelp around their bodies to keep from drifting while they sleep, and will give birth to their young in the water. Sea otters can eat a quarter of their weight each day in urchins, crabs, chitons, clams and octopus. Sometimes, while floating on their backs, they crack open the shells of their prey by smashing them against rocks balanced on their chests.

Sea otters' fur is denser than that of any other animal in the world and keeps them dry. Once known as "soft gold," its luxuriance was one of the main reasons Russian and English traders first came to this area. Due to over-hunting, sea otters were completely eliminated from the Washington coast by the early 1900s, but re-introduction efforts have been successful. In spite of recent oil spills, there are now more than 300 otters and their population is increasing about 15 percent each year.

A CHANGING COASTLINE

Summer's relatively calm surf is replaced by the violent fury of winter storms. Thirty-foot waves smash into the rocks and toss huge drifting trees about like toothpicks. Air and water are forced into cracks, literally exploding rock away from the headlands. Ground to sand, the bones of the headlands eventually come to rest on the beaches they once protected.

The seashore is in constant change. The sand castle you build at the water's edge is quickly reclaimed by the water. If you could look back in time you would see that the entire coastline is just as ephemeral—moving back and forth like the waves themselves. The prairies around the town of Forks, now several miles from the ocean, were once ancient estuaries formed when the water was higher.

In some places, the coast is eroding as much as 100 feet every thirty years. Remnants of the old coastline can be seen in the thousands of islands and seastacks that guard the shore. The rocks left standing are more resistant to erosion, but in time they succumb to the force of the waves. Headlands become islands that are gradually whittled into lonely seastacks and pinnacles. Many ships have foundered on these rocks, and headlands still pose a danger to hikers who do not pay close attention to tide charts.

Seals and sea lions haul out on exposed rocks at the base of the cliffs to rest, while clouds of nesting birds whirl above. Thousands of murres and cormorants raise their young in rookeries on the near-vertical rock faces to avoid predators. Most of the soil that carpets the tops of these seastacks and islands was formed when they were part of coast. The clown-like tufted puffin and its relative, the rhinoceros auklet, protect their chicks from hungry gulls and ravens by digging nesting burrows in this dirt. Both birds literally fly underwater, using their sleek wings to chase small fish.

Peregrine falcons and bald eagles keep watchful eyes on the activity below. Both can catch seabirds in flight, but eagles also scavenge the beaches and tide-pools for an easy meal. The Olympic Peninsula is one of the few remaining strongholds of these endangered species in the conterminous United States.

LIFE AT THE EDGE

The bedrock that is exposed when the tide goes out is one of the richest, most diverse habitats on the peninsula. The intertidal zone is like a busy city teeming with life—and death. Different seaweeds, anemones, urchins, mussels and barnacles cling tenaciously to every available inch of space and to each other. Many animals graze on the algae, while hunters such as seastars and whelks lurk about for their next meal.

The intertidal zone can be divided into bands of communities that are shaped by wave strength, surface type and degree of exposure to air and predators. These varied environments—ranging from the lower intertidal to the spray zone—are miniature ecosystems. Scientists study ecological principles here that can be applied to many of our terrestrial habitats.

Mussels are one of the most tenacious and competitive animals of the intertidal zone. Although usually smaller, mature California mussels may grow as long as eight to twelve inches. Unchecked, they will dominate much of the rocky surface, but they also provide habitat for over 300 other species of life.

Ochre sea stars (or starfish) are one of the mussels' main predators, and often limit the lower extent of mussel communities. Sea stars give new meaning to the words "eating out." First, they envelope individual mussels and pry them open with their tubed feet. As soon as they open the shell wide enough, the sea star literally places its stomach inside the shell and digests the tissue from the inside out. Sea anemones benefit from the leftovers that may drift their way.

Smaller mussels and barnacles are prey for shell-boring snails like the whelk. Whelks use rasp-like tongue, or *radula*, and acidic secretions, to bore holes in their victims' shells. Once through, they insert their radula and scrape the soft tissues out.

When the tide is low enough, black oystercatchers will also make a meal of a mussel. They insert their long chisel-like beaks into the bivalve and quickly snip the muscles that clamp the shells together. These noisy birds also eat limpets and other invertebrates. They lay their eggs on rocky or cobbly areas of the beach, and are easily disturbed by humans. Oystercatchers' abundance indicates the health of the intertidal ecosystem.

Seastars and anemones, common intertidal life along the Olympic coast.

Intertidal organisms must be extremely tough to withstand the pounding surf and drying sun. Some occupants are exceptionally old—urchins and mussels can live for at least 50 years while it is possible that some sea anemones may reach a ripe age of 1,000!

In spite of intertidal animals' hardiness, people can easily damage them. Mussel colonies are damaged by floating debris and strong waves, but aquatic plants and animals naturally recolonize these areas. Some surf fisherman scrape off bucketfuls

The orca is often thought of as the "wolf of the sea." Orcas usually hunt in pods and communicate with each other through a series of whistles, clicking sounds, and screams.

of mussels to gather ribbon worms, hidden among them, for bait. Clusters of large, colony-dwelling tube worms are also harvested. Areas damaged by humans in this manner may take decades to regenerate. The intertidal zone was added to Olympic National Park in the late 1980s and collecting this live bait now is prohibited within park boundaries. It is still commonly practiced, however, along the remainder of the coast. Some intertidal animals are also considered delicacies by various cultures, and are harvested for food on the peninsula.

Human tidepool explorers must be careful where they step. Taking animals like sea stars home as mementos is no different from taking a wild squirrel or bird from

the forest. It is far better to look at interesting life than to pick it up. Studies in Chile have shown that an amazing species recovery can occur if humans are fenced out of intertidal areas.

SHIFTING SANDS

In some places, especially along the southern coast of the peninsula, fine sands settle out of the surf, increasing the beach size. Without rocks to grasp, life forms are less visible, but still present buried in the sand. Razor clams and sand dollars strain food from the water, while Dungeness crabs and snails patrol the seafloor. Waves wash smelt onto the beaches, where they lay and fertilize their eggs.

Walking along the sand, it's hard to imagine the number of tiny invertebrate animals that live underfoot, but the probing beaks of sandpipers and other shorebirds easily find them. Most beaches here are wide and flat—in places the sand is compact enough that people drive their cars on it. If vehicles are driven too near the water at low tide, they can damage clam beds.

MUDDY WATERS

Wherever rivers enter the sea, they carry part of the earth's soil swept from the forest floor. Nutrients and sediments settle onto mudflats where fresh and saltwater mix. Shifting currents build up sand bars that form protective estuaries—one of the richest habitats on earth. Here young salmon stop over on their journey to the open sea. Millions of migrating waterfowl feed on small crustaceans and molluscs buried in the mud. Underwater prairies of eelgrass hide vast schools of herring—another link in the food chain that ultimately supports us.

The southern boundary of the peninsula is formed by the Chehalis River. This river was the main drainage system of the glacial lobe that filled the Puget Trough. During the Ice Age it probably rivaled the size of the Columbia River. The massive amounts of gravel and sediment it carried helped form Grays Harbor—one of the large estuaries along the Washington coast. Now a busy industrial center, this harbor still plays a vital role in the survival of many species.

ANCIENT DRIFTWOOD

Winter storms may dump several inches of rain in one day along the peninsula's coast. Raging waters undercut riverbanks, causing huge old-growth trees to fall into the torrent. Some of these logs remain on bars in the river, while others are swept down to the ocean. There they can act like battering rams, smashing mussel beds and other invertebrates, creating a diverse successional pattern among the intertidal community. The huge logs are also potentially deadly for unwary humans swimming or playing in the surf.

Floated ashore by high tides or storms, a micro-ecosystem of small animals develops around them. Drifting logs from the peninsula have been carried by currents around the Pacific. Hawaiians built dugout canoes from ancient fir logs that washed upon their shores.

Seastacks arranged off the tip of Toleak Point in Olympic National Park.

Morning light over Dungeness National Wildlife Refuge along the Strait of Juan de Fuca.

Sea urchins at low tide in the Tongue Point Marine Sanctuary, Clallam County.

THE INLAND SEA

Seawater followed the retreat of the continental glaciers creating Puget Sound, the Strait of Juan de Fuca, and the straits between Vancouver Island and the main land. Here there are over 2,100 miles of inland shoreline and rich communities of aquatic and intertidal life.

In many places, the bluffs above the beaches are composed of unconsolidated pebbles, gravel and sand left behind by the glaciers. An occasional mammoth tooth or mastodon tusk falls out of the eroding cliffs, the loose rocky material that gives birth to the shoreline. Currents may tease and carry away the sand, leaving pebble beaches: good habitat for hardshell clams. Great blue herons stand motionless in the water waiting to spear unwary tidbits.

Protection Island, northeast of the town of Sequim, is formed from the same glacial leftovers. The sandy cliffs, grassy slopes and isolation create ideal nesting habitat. Nearly three quarters of the seabirds in Puget Sound nest on this one is-land, including 17,000 pairs of rhinoceros auklets. Once threatened by grazing and housing developments, this area is now protected as a national wildlife refuge.

Sediments from the Elwha and Dungeness river systems combine with erosional debris from bluffs to form two large spits. These arms of sand protect bays used by both commercial interests and myriad wildlife.

In some areas bedrock meets the water, creating habitat similar to that found on the coast, but with less wave action. River otters, sea lions, and harbor seals hunt along the shoreline. Gray and minke whales infrequently visit the sound and it was once the home of humpbacks. Porpoises and pods of orca (killer whales) still patrol the inland sea.

Above: *Shi Shi Beach sunset along the coast of Olympic National Park.*

———— ✳ ————

Facing page: *Late afternoon sun bisects a pair of seastacks along the Olympic coast.*

OF SPECIAL CONCERN

The fabric of the peninsula's marine ecosystem can be rent in many ways. Over the last decade, we have learned how healthful seafood can be for us. But what is good for the human body may not always be good for the whole. Native oysters have been harvested to the point they are becoming increasingly rare. Red sea urchins are heavily exploited for their gonads, considered a delicacy in Japan. A variety of fleets have overfished the high seas and local waters, contributing to dramatic decreases in many fish populations.

Many fishermen believe they compete for the dwindling fish stocks with the area's seals and sea lions. Studies show that the majority of species of fish and inver-

Left: *Dense concentration of goose barnacles and a solitary mussel along the Strait of Juan de Fuca.*

——— ✳ ———

Facing page: *The intertidal zone has a variety of algae including sea lettuce and sea sac.*

tebrates these animals eat are not commercially valuable. In open waters, healthy salmon are too fast for most mammals to catch. Some animals have learned, however, that salmon are easier to catch in areas where they congregate during their yearly migrations—especially near artificial obstructions like shipping locks or nets. It can be very frustrating to have a salmon stolen out of your net or off your line before you are able to reel it in. Many people now advocate reducing seal populations, but researchers have pointed out that these animals may also eat other fish that prey on young salmon.

Now protected by law, harbor seal populations can increase between five and fifteen percent each year. Shellfish harvesting has been closed in a few areas along Hood Canal due to seal fecal contamination of the water. This has occurred in shellfish beds that are very close to seal haulouts. Management agencies have had some success using fences to relocate haulout sites.

Fairly large oil spills have coated the peninsula's beaches three times in the last decade. Research so far shows that although thousands of individual birds and some mammals have died, damage to the coastline after extensive clean-up efforts appears minimal. The oil that washed onto the *outer* coast was less toxic than the unrefined crude oil that tankers carry.

These spills have been small, however, compared to the Exxon *Valdez* disaster in which 11 million gallons of oil flowed into Alaska's Prince William Sound. As many as 500,000 birds and hundreds of mammals died because of this one incident. The potential for a similar spill exists here each day as fully-laden tankers steer through the Strait of Juan de Fuca en route to refineries. Over 6.5 billion gallons of

Above: *A mosaic of barnacles, mussels, and other marine life encrusts rocks along the coast. Clusters of aggregating anemones fill channels in the foreground.*

———— ✳ ————

Facing page: *Seahair drapes uplifted layers of sedimentary rocks at Point of Arches.*

oil are transported to Puget Sound each year. The long-term ecological effects of oil in marine systems is still unknown.

Companies and government agencies have proposed offshore drilling for oil and gas along the peninsula's continental shelf. Recent geological surveys, though, indicate little oil may be present.

Ships from foreign ports pump out bilge water that contains a host of exotic aquatic plants and animals, many of which survive. Tons of litter wash onto the coastline every year, ranging from tennis shoes to military missiles. Navy jets used offshore sea lion rocks in Copalis National Wildlife Refuge for bomber training, but halted this practice in 1993.

One of the biggest impacts to the marine environment comes from our individual activity on land. Every time we start our car or flush the toilet we begin a chain of events that influences the world around us. The actions of each of us, whether doctor, student or ditchdigger, have consequences. When measured by the collective weight of the millions of humans that live in the area, the pressure can be enormous.

The city of Victoria on Vancouver Island flushes all of its raw, untreated sewage directly into the Strait each year. Research has shown that so far this dumping has caused little damage, due to the tremendous currents that flow by the city—but the future is uncertain. The herbicides, pesticides and fertilizers we spray on our lawns, along with many of the hazardous products we use around the household, eventually flow into the marine ecosystem.

Industrial discharge combines with our waste to create a toxic "soup" that settles into the water. Copper, lead, arsenic, zinc, cadmium, mercury, and PCBs are among the chemicals that have been found in the sediment of Puget Sound. While the ocean has an enormous capacity to clean itself, there is a limit to how much we can pollute without causing serious consequence. Concentrations of poisonous chemicals have accumulated in animals, from porpoises to peregrine falcons. Parts of Puget Sound are posted with signs that warn: "Bottomfish, crab and shellfish may be unsafe to eat due to pollution."

We can all take steps to reduce the damage. Water quality agencies recommend limiting pollution by driving less, conserving water and electricity, and reducing use of hazardous household materials. These sound like simple steps, although implementing them in our daily lives can be challenging.

The longest stretch of wild coastline in the conterminous U.S. is protected by Olympic National Park. Many of the outer islands and seastacks are part of the National Wildlife Refuge system, but there are still many threats to the marine ecosystem here and along the inland sea. A proposed National Marine Sanctuary along the west side of the peninsula would prohibit oil and gas drilling, as well as offshore undersea mining operations. Shipping lanes would be moved farther away from the coast to prevent the likelihood of oil spills reaching the shoreline. Such a sanctuary would help the many different agencies involved manage this area as an ecosystem.

These rich resources are tied to the land and to ourselves in ways we are just beginning to understand. With care, the sea can help feed our hungry nations. It can also be a home where humpback and blue whales ply the waters once again.

Evening repose, Shi Shi Beach, Olympic National Park.

Above: *Second Beach, south of LaPush, Olympic National Park.*

---　✳　---

Facing page: *View toward the Pacific Ocean from Taylor Point, Olympic National Park.*

Above: *The North American bald eagle makes its home along the coast and rivers of the greater Olympic ecosystem.*

——— ✳ ———

Facing page: *Driftwood, Rialto Beach on the Olympic coast.*

Above: *Beach pattern accented by sunset along the Olympic coast.*

———— ✳ ————

Facing page: *View across the freshwater Ruby Creek as it flows into the Pacific Ocean north of Kalaloch.*

*S*hafts of light fall across the forest floor, highlighting tiny castles of moss.

The eerie trill of a varied thrush echoes among the trees—answered by a

distant raven. We are climbing through a living cathedral of massive trees.

Gnarled roots form living steps that allow us to ascend to the lake.

Exhausted by the trail's steepness, we stop to rest at the base of an ancient

monarch. The tree's life seems to envelop me. It's hard to comprehend the

centuries these trees have witnessed; this tree was already a hundred years

old when Columbus landed in the "new land." But here in the forest,

leaning against a root thicker than my chest, time seems within grasp.

A few feet away, an inch-high seedling sprouts atop a fallen brother. What

will life be like 300 years from now, when this young tree finally penetrates

the forest canopy?

A THOUSAND SHADES OF GREEN

———————— ✳ ————————

Primeval forests once cloaked the peninsula from beach to mountaintop. A vast army of conifers dominated the landscape, mediators between earth and sky. But this has not always been the case. Thousands of years ago, glaciers accomplished what humans have at times threatened to do—ice scoured away every last bit of vegetation that lay in its path.

Lodgepole pine forests invaded first. Douglas fir didn't arrive on the scene until about 10,000 to 12,000 years ago and the Western red cedar is a relative newcomer, establishing itself within the last 5,000 years.

Conifers outcompete broadleaf trees over most of the peninsula for a number of reasons. Many trees may limit their photosynthesis during the summer's long dry spells. But conifers can produce food during spring and fall, giving them an advantage over the leafless deciduous trees.

The natural forests of the peninsula are more diverse and complex than we could have imagined a few decades ago. Studies are just now beginning to unlock some of the secrets of this guarded realm. The largest representative trees of several species are found here, some taller than the length of a football field. The trunk of the record red cedar is more than 60 feet around at the base.

One of the most interesting discoveries has been the role the lowly mushroom plays in helping these giants attain their size. The mushrooms we are familiar with are really the reproductive organs of a fungus that lives underground or in decaying trees. Many mushrooms, or fruiting bodies, can belong to one massive fungus.

Researchers found there are far more different kinds of fungus in the forest than higher plants and that nearly all above-ground plants are associated with a fungus in some way. Over 2,000 different species of fungus are affiliated with Douglas fir around the world.

The moist vernal habitat of skunk cabbage, Quinault River Valley.

The fungus's hair-like filaments join with the tree's root hairs to form new structures called mycorrhizae. This marriage benefits both the fungus and the tree. Mycorrhizae help the tree absorb water and nutrients. Some produce enzymes that promote root growth and antibiotics that ward off tree disease. The tree, in turn, sends as much as one half of the carbohydrates it produces through photosynthesis down to the roots where the fungus can absorb some of the food.

This underground network of roots and mycorrhizae can connect individual trees together, even of different species. Some biologists feel this link can turn a forest into a functioning organism, rather than a collection of separate entities.

Whether or not all trees in a natural forest are physically connected, they do function together to moderate the weather. Forests are generally cooler on hot days and warmer when it's cold. This allows a number of species to survive that would normally not be able to in a more exposed environment.

The amount of mycorrhizae in an old-growth forest is astonishing—5,000 pounds per acre. Not all fungi help trees, though. Laminated root rot can live sixty to eighty years and kills large patches of Douglas fir and hemlock. Some fungi are even carnivores—they attract insect larvae, and then kill and digest them.

Across the peninsula, differences in temperature, moisture and weather patterns separate the forest into broad zones, and these areas can be subdivided into smaller groups of typical plant associations. Like the bands of life in the intertidal, these zones extend from the coastline to the high mountains. As a rough rule, every 500 feet you gain in elevation is similar to venturing 100 miles north. Climbing from sea level to the top of Mt. Olympus, at 7,965 feet, would be similar to driving from Port Angeles to the Arctic. In the Olympics, treeline is lower than it is in the Cascades because of heavy snowfall, especially on the west side of the Olympic National Park.

The wide range in precipitation from east to west makes the distinctions between some of the zones less clear. Although many animals and plants range through nearly all of the major zones, each community has species that are mainly associated with it. Each zone can also be broken down into smaller sub-units with specific tree, bush and flower associations, but these are beyond the scope of this book.

FORESTS OF RAIN

You are surrounded by life when you enter a rain forest. Even children are prone to be quiet, feeling they have come upon a fairyland where sprites and wood elves play. Rain forests bring to mind images of lush tropical jungles. Tropical rain forests developed over millennium in relatively warm climates, allowing tens of thousands of individual species to evolve. The northwest's temperate rain forests, while lower in species numbers, have more biological material than any ecosystem in the world—as much as 1 million pounds per acre.

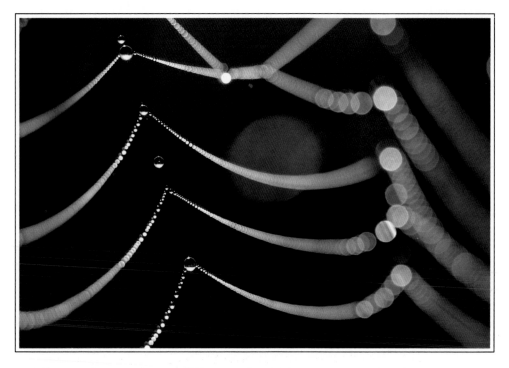

The rain forest valleys on the west side of Olympic National Park are some of the most spectacular examples of the Sitka spruce community that stretches along the coast from Oregon to Alaska. Several other temperate rain forests are found in isolated areas throughout the world.

Sitka spruce and western hemlock are trees mainly associated with the rain forest, although western red cedar, Douglas fir and big-leaf maple are also common. Rain forest valleys were formerly occupied by alpine glaciers that yielded tremendous amounts of water and gravel. As the glaciers receded, their rivers cut different levels of terraces through the outwash. Each terrace supports a diverse mix of plant and animal species.

Sitka spruce will thrive only in wet, foggy conditions near the coast, as their needles cannot regulate the amount of water they lose through them. The three main rainforest valleys (Hoh, Queets, Quinault) average around 12 feet of moisture each year. This precipitation is supplemented by thick fogs that move in from the ocean. Conifer needles act like nets, condensing extra moisture from the air and adding as many as 30 additional inches of water annually. Additionally, each large conifer can store thousands of gallons of water in its massive trunk.

The abundant rainfall and relatively mild climate create a profusion of green. Plants and animals live on top of each other—every square inch of ground is covered, along with many of the branches and foliage overhead. A plethora of microscopic plants and animals live on the needles of a conifer. Known as "scuzz," these organisms fix nitrogen, produce insecticides, and provide food for a chain of insect predators that may ultimately protect the tree from other leaf-eating insects. This could be one of the reasons why natural old-growth forests can better withstand insect attacks than can managed forests.

On a larger scale, epiphytes, or "plants that grow on plants" are more visible to the human eye and are one of the rain forests' main attractions, especially in big-leaf maple groves. Festoons of clubmoss several feet long drape the maples. Some

Above: *Vine maple draped with club mosses and other mosses in the Hoh Rain Forest. These epiphytes, or plants that live upon plants, do not hurt the maples, but can provide a number of benefits to the host trees.*

———— ✳ ————

Facing page: *Spiderweb on Mt. Walker, Olympic National Forest.*

botanists feel that clubmosses, mosses, lichens, liverworts and licorice ferns grow more abundantly on maples because the trees are deciduous. In winter, the maple's leafless branches provide a perfect platform for epiphytes to receive more light. Others credit the qualities of the maple's bark for the profusion of growth.

Epiphytes obtain their own nutrients from air and rainfall and do not harm the tree except when their sheer weight causes a branch to break. But maples and a few other tree species send adventitious roots into the dense epiphytic mats to glean nutrients from them. Over 130 species of epiphytes have been found in the rain forest.

Competition for space on the forest floor is keen. When a tree falls, its surface is fair game for plants. Low pioneering mosses may colonize the nurselogs first and provide seedbeds for young tree saplings. Taller mosses may eventually out-compete the seedlings and nearly all the young trees die as the bark gradually sloughs off. The log is then recolonized by a new generation of mosses and seedlings. The trees that survive eventually send roots to the soil and, as the nurselog decays, the tree appears to be standing on stilts. A "colonnade," or straight row of trees, in the forest gives away the presence of a long-fallen companion.

Most of the seedlings that survive on a nurselog are Sitka spruce, their sharp needles less palatable to elk than those of the western hemlock. Roosevelt elk are the forest's gardeners—their selective tastes can tip the balance and help alter the entire make-up of the valley bottoms. The National Park Service built a series of elk exclosures to study the effects elk have on the forest. Inside, where elk cannot reach, a thick tangle of ferns, huckleberry and hemlock saplings grows quickly. Outside the exclosures, grasses tend to dominate much of the forest floor. Elk create open glades that are easy for elk, and humans, to travel through.

Roosevelt elk are the largest subspecies of elk in North America, weighing as much as 1,000 pounds. They range from Vancouver Island to the redwoods of northern California, and the largest wild herds roam across the Olympics. Some animals remain in rain forest valleys year-round, but others migrate to the high country during summer months.

The west side of the peninsula is now home to several thousand elk, but this has not always been the case. Early market hunters decimated herds for hides. The animal's two canine teeth were popular throughout the nation as watchfobs, which further hastened the destruction. One resident boasted about killing 70 elk in one day near Lake Ozette.

In 1904, congressmen introduced a bill to establish "Elk National Park," but it failed to pass due to a debate over whether the elks' winter habitat, considered valuable timberland, should be set aside as part of the park. President Theodore Roosevelt was able to establish Olympic National Monument in 1909. This monument was to be administered by the United States Forest Service primarily for protecting elk.

During the first part of the century, Washington State also banned all elk hunt-

Shade-tolerant western hemlock, Quinault Rain Forest.

ing, and started a bounty program for predators. At that time, game conservationists were concerned that large predators, like wolves and cougar, posed a threat to the few remaining elk. Because of the anti-predator campaign, wolves could no longer be found on the peninsula after the mid-1920s.

Hunters can now harvest elk on the peninsula, but alter herd composition by killing the largest bulls. Hunting inside the national park is prohibited, and many elk die from long winters and malnutrition. Cougars will attack healthy elk, but usually target sick or young animals, killing them by jumping on their backs and biting through their spinal columns or snapping their necks. These secretive cats range across the entire peninsula from coast to mountaintop.

Although cougars are rarely seen, more people have reported encounters with them the last few years—such as when a visitor was strolling along a popular rain forest nature trail and one dropped out of a tree behind him. No one has been injured in the Olympics, but cougars have attacked children on Vancouver Island where suburbs are spreading into the animals' prime habitat. Incidences of cougars harming humans are extremely unusual, but park rangers now ask hikers to keep small children close by on some trails. People should feel lucky if they catch a glimpse of these magnificent animals.

Many other herbivores live in the rain forest besides elk. The lowly banana slug is found throughout the lowlands. Most people avoid slugs, and most people don't like them in their gardens. Unless you live in the forest, the slugs you are most likely to discover around your home are one of several species that were accidently introduced from Europe.

Banana slugs are able to reproduce prodigiously as each animal has male and female sexual organs. When mating, each animal fertilizes the other. At times, slugs become so entangled they need to gnaw their male organs off to break free. Slugs evolved from snails; the mild rainy climate allows them to live without the protection of a shell.

The rain forest valley floors are moist enough that fires rarely occur. Large stand-destroying fires may happen every 600 to 1,500 years. Wind is the leading cause of tree death in these forests—ultimately killing about 80 percent of the trees.

THE GREAT LOWLAND FORESTS

The vast empire of the lowland forest stretches above the rain forest valley bottoms and inland from the Pacific Ocean. Although there are a few exceptions, given enough time, western hemlock probably would dominate over other tree species in most areas of the lowland zone. Hemlocks carpet the forest floor with an amazing number of seeds each year. Young trees grow well in shade—the needles of a six-inch–diameter hemlock (twenty feet tall) usually provide over 10,000 square feet of

Evergreen canopy on the east side of the greater ecosystem in the Quilcene River watershed of
Olympic National Forest.

Above: *Elk-browsed understory of the old-growth Hoh Rain Forest.*

———— ✳ ————

Facing page: *Roots reach for the ground from a nurse log, Olympic National Forest.*

leaf surface, twice that of a Douglas fir. This ability to gather light on the dim forest floor allows hemlocks to grow in the shade of the larger Douglas firs. If left undisturbed, the Douglas fir would eventually die and be replaced by the hemlocks.

Still, the lowlands of western Washington and Oregon are more commonly known as the Douglas fir region. Expansive stands of hemlock are uncommon due to natural and human disturbance. Large fires occurred every few hundred years on the drier east side of the Olympics. These fires created sunlit areas where Douglas fir seedlings took hold and gradually matured into massive groves. Large fires also burned much of the wide plain between the Olympic Mountains and the coast. And it was here that hurricane-force winds toppled huge swaths of trees in 1921 and 1962. Millions of conifers fell in these storms.

Grand fir is scattered throughout the lowland forest on the drier north and east sides of the peninsula. Western red cedar is fairly common in both the Sitka spruce and the lowland forest zones, even in drier areas. Groves of pure cedar thrive in wetter spots near swamps, bogs, and ravines. The cedar's arrival 5,000 years ago may have heralded the development of many cultural advances in the coastal Native American way of life.

Even though Native Americans used cedar extensively, they had little impact on the peninsula's forests. A number of the first western homesteaders learned medicinal and practical uses for forest plants from local Indians, but for the most part, the giant trees were obstacles to farming and travel. The western part of the peninsula was generally considered "unfit" for agriculture and people began to view timber as a valuable resource.

When walking through a second-growth forest, it's hard not to notice huge stumps—ghosts of the past. Many giant conifers of the lowland valleys were cut by hand. Notches in the stumps held springboards where men stood while they chopped and sawed. Loggers first worked inland from the bays and coast. On the south side of the peninsula, rivers were used as "log highways." Temporary dams were built that, when broken, created man-made floods to sweep the enormous logs to the mills.

The lumber from Sitka spruce was light and strong, ideal material for World War I biplanes. To ensure an adequate supply, the army formed the "Spruce Production Division" and quickly built a thirty-six–mile railroad on the north peninsula. The war ended before the first log was shipped. But the Spruce Railroad, along with trains running on hundreds of miles of additional track built by private companies, carried logs until most of the accessible old growth in the lowlands had been cut. With the advent of the logging truck, loggers could move onto the steeper, more remote hillsides, and by the middle of the twentieth century, nearly all of the peninsula's original lowland forests had been cut.

THE FOREST PRIMEVAL

Despite natural disruptions like fire and wind, stands of Douglas fir, western hemlock, Sitka spruce and western red cedar can be extremely long-lived. Individual cedars can grow for 1,000 years, while Douglas fir can live for 700 years. Biologists estimate that, in the prehistoric northwest, roughly two thirds of the forest was "old growth." These forests develop old-growth characteristics after they have been growing for two to three hundred years. The presence of large, old trees is one of the old-growth forest's primary features. Another is a mixture of conifer species of many ages that create different tree heights. Known as a multi-layered canopy, this characteristic provides rich wildlife habitat.

Death creates another fundamental part of an old-growth ecosystem. Winter winds literally blow the tops off a number of giant conifers each year. This begins a process of decay that may last for hundreds of years as different types of fungi, bacteria, and insects attack and slowly digest the tree. The plate-like growths protruding from the side of a snag are the reproductive bodies of fungi. It's hard to walk through an old forest without being covered with spores falling from these "conks."

As they rot, large snags become apartment houses for many types of life. Douglas fir decomposes from the outside, making it easy for small birds like the chestnut-backed chickadee and red-breasted nuthatch to use them. Many of the other trees, especially red cedar, rot from the inside out. Large pileated woodpeckers, a relative of the nearly extinct ivory-billed woodpecker, favor these trees for roosting and nesting, as it is easier for them to hammer into the hollow cavities.

Big-leaf and vine maple display autumn colors in the Elwha River bottomland.

When snags finally fall to the ground, they join trees that were uprooted by wind to form the last main feature of old growth. Ancient forests are littered with fallen trees that fulfill a variety of functions for wildlife: dams, bridges, homes, water reservoirs, farms, and hunting grounds. These logs last for centuries, and often support more life on the ground then they did when they were alive. The soils of these forests are relatively poor in nutrition—it's primarily the above-ground material that provides the biological richness unique to this community.

On hillsides, logs collect litter above them and limit erosion. Various animals use these logs as quick pathways through the forest, and many small creatures live inside them. Rotten logs act as sponges and absorb great quantities of water. Researchers have found roots from surrounding live trees penetrating and absorbing moisture from "dead" logs. Many wet logs survive wildfires and are full of fungal spores that help reinoculate the forest.

Old-growth forests are biological banks, rich with diversity. They are the primary home of the now infamous spotted owl. Although these owls have been found in younger forest stands, they need a forest with old-growth characteristics to successfully breed and thrive as a species. Just as humans can survive in the Antarctic, spotted owls can subsist for a time in new forests. Exceptions to this have been found in parts of northern California and the eastern Washington Cascades where forests may develop some old-growth features at a younger age.

The multi-layered canopies in old growth provide hunting perches for the spotted owl and protection from predators like the goshawk and great horned owl. One of the spotted owl's main sources of food on the peninsula is the northern flying squirrel. Squirrels are the acrobats of the forests—they do not actually fly, but glide at night from tree to tree and down to the ground in search of truffles. These underground mushrooms rely on squirrels and other mammals to distribute their spores through the forest via the animals' scat. Such spores may even pass through the owls after they eat a squirrel, and be spread over a larger territory. The fungi complete the cycle by developing mycorrhizal relations that help trees to grow into towering giants.

Marbled murrelets, small robin-sized seabirds, also depend on old-growth trees for rearing their young in the Pacific Northwest. Here they nest almost exclusively on well developed platforms of lichen and moss that grow on large old-growth branches. In these nests, often a hundred feet above the ground, a pair of adults raises one chick. The parents leave the nest before dawn to fly out to the sea—as far as 50 miles—and return with small fish. Unlike other seabirds, they are camouflaged brown and white in the summer to blend into the forest. Murrelets are more abundant in Alaska, where they also nest in old-growth spruce forests. A few build nests on the open tundra near the coast.

Huge hollow snags provide communal nesting sites for the Vaux's swift. After they fledge and take wing, young swifts spend most of their lives in the air. They can sleep and even mate while flying and may fly as far as 600 miles in one day. Some types of bats also depend on the cracks and crevices of old-growth trees for roosting sites, and several other animals are closely associated with, but not dependent upon, old growth for their survival.

OPENINGS IN THE FOREST

Unique smaller treeless habitats are scattered throughout the peninsula lowlands . Small prairies can be found on the west side, which were maintained in part by Native Americans who regularly burned them to more easily obtain game and promote the growth of the blue camas. Camas bulbs were relished by tribes, although as noted by an early explorer, "…when eaten in a large quantity they occa-

Lake Crescent—the second-largest freshwater body in Olympic National Park—with Mt. Storm King in the distance.

sion bowel complaints…Assuredly they produce flatulence: when in the Indian hut I was almost blown out by strength of wind."

Homesteaders found these small prairies much easier to farm than old-growth areas where they had to fell enormous trees and remove stumps. In the rain shadow on the northeast side of the peninsula around Sequim, open grasslands are interspersed with Garry oaks. Because this area is so dry, farmers developed a network of irrigation canals to distribute water.

Hundreds of small lakes, along with a few large ones, dot the peninsula. Lake Crescent was formed after an arm of the continental glacier pushed up through the lower foothills. The water that filled the resulting hole is at least six hundred feet deep, and may be a thousand feet deep in spots. Isolated for thousands of years, Lake Crescent's cutthroat and rainbow trout evolved into separate stocks, the Beardsley trout and the crescenti trout. Beardsleys can weigh over twenty pounds.

A smaller, but no less distinctive, fish is the tiny Olympic mudminnow. Mudminnows are a potentially threatened species due to habitat destruction. They prefer quiet ponds and can be found only on the Olympic Peninsula.

Shallow bogs, marshes and other wetlands host plants and animals adapted to these special environments. Natural cranberry bogs were highly coveted by Native American tribes. These wetlands also provide resting spots for tens of thousands of migrating waterfowl during their annual migrations. They are extremely productive and contribute much to the peninsula's overall biological richness.

RUNNING WATER

The seeps and side streams that lace the forest are home for a variety of salamanders and young salmon. Woody debris, especially large old-growth logs, provides shelter and protection from predators. These logs create eddies that protect young fish during flooding and nurture whole communities of small invertebrates. If you flick a conifer needle into a quiet pool, several tiny salmon may dash to the surface hoping to find a fallen insect.

It's hard to imagine that one of these two-inch fish may fight its way back up a river as a twenty- or thirty-pound adult. Female salmon lay two to six thousand eggs, of which ten to twenty percent hatch. When old enough, the juvenile fish swim down to the ocean where they begin incredible migrations. Depending on the species, salmon may stay in the open sea from one to seven years and can range as far north as the Aleutian Islands.

Only a handful of salmon survive the gauntlet of natural and human predators to return and spawn. One writer likened the fish to "ziplock bags of nutrients"—carrying the richness of the ocean back into the mountains. After the fish spawn, their carcasses litter the riverbanks. Researchers found that at least twenty-two different birds and

Free-flowing section of the Elwha River between the impounded waters of Lake Aldwell and Lake Mills.

Vine maple amidst old-growth forest in Olympic National Forest near Quinault River.

mammals feed directly on dead salmon. Bears and bald eagles were common, but smaller species from winter wrens to Douglas squirrels also benefited. These little animals, in turn, travel away from the streams, providing food for larger predators.

Rivers possess an unseen element that we are just beginning to understand. Water does not stop at the stream bottom, but seeps below the riverbed into the surrounding land into an area known as the hyporheic. This area is rich in nutrients and supports numerous tiny aquatic creatures.

IN THE CLOUDS

Each spring and fall, the skies above the forest are filled with migrating birds. Some species that pass through may make roundtrip journeys as long as 22,000 miles each year. Birds migrate to the peninsula, or use it as a resting stop on their way to Canada and Alaska. Populations of a number of migrant bird species are decreasing due to forest fragmentation and loss of wetlands that is occurring throughout North and South America.

Several thousand raptors are sighted at Cape Flattery each March and April. Over a dozen species are sighted, but red-tailed hawks, sharp-shinned hawks, and bald eagles are the most common. The birds use the thermals and winds to gain enough height to attempt a safe crossing of the thirteen-mile Strait of Juan de Fuca. Groups of as many as 300 or 400 turkey vultures may cross the strait at a single time, closer to Port Angeles.

OF SPECIAL CONCERN

There are other animals on the Olympic Peninsula that cause, or have caused, great concern. Within the last few years, ships from Asia carried a species of gypsy moth that has the potential to devastate the forests. Gypsy moths imported from the east coast do little damage to *conifers*, but Asian gypsy moths can.

A primary predator, the wolf, is missing from Olympic National Park. One of the goals of the National Park Service is to restore native ecosystems and species within parks to the diversity that existed before western culture and civilization influenced them. Many people fear for their safety when wolves are discussed, but there has never been a documented case of a healthy wolf attacking a person in North America. Few people walk the woods in fear of cougar, even though they are fairly common here. While the park has no current plans for reintroducing the wolf, it remains a possibility for future study.

Finally, restoring diminishing salmon runs on the peninsula is a major goal of several different agencies responsible for managing these fisheries. Many biologists feel that habitat destruction, overfishing, and introduction of non-native hatchery fish into streams have been the main reasons for drastic declines in most runs.

These agencies have joined together with the Elwha Klallam tribe to study ways to restore fisheries to the Lower Elwha River ecosystem, dammed since 1910. The two hydroelectric dams were built without fish passage, even though it had been required by Washington State law since 1890. The Elwha drainage forms the heart of Olympic National Park and this river was once a vital artery that carried nutrients back from the sea. Chinook salmon weighing as much as 100 pounds fought their way into the mountains. And as many as ten different stocks of anadromous fish used the river throughout the different months of the year.

After several years of study, the agencies jointly recommended removing the two dams on the river as the only way of fully restoring the ecosystem. Unlike the peninsula's other major river systems, all but eight of the Elwha's seventy-five river miles are protected within Olympic National Park. Fisheries biologists feel the 175,000 acres of protected drainage habitat in the park gives the Elwha a much higher potential for restoration than other rivers on the peninsula. If the plan is successful, returning fish would bring as much as hundreds of thousands of pounds of biomass, or organic material, up the river each year—fertilizing the entire Elwha drainage. Dam removal would also restore sacred land to the Elwha tribe.

Congress passed the Elwha River Ecosystem and Fisheries Restoration Act in 1992, directing a report to determine the best way to fully restore the Elwha's salmon runs. Although the legislation did not satisfy any single interest fully, the owners of the dams and all parties affected by the potential removal agreed on this legislation. Engineers feel the sediment that has collected behind the dams can be managed with a variety of techniques as the reservoir is lowered. The major concern that remains is the high cost of the removal project, but even this has the potential to bring jobs into the area.

More agencies are moving towards catch-and-release programs (where anglers release fish instead of taking them home) to protect wild fish stocks. In other areas of the country these efforts have dramatically improved recreational fishing. Several other rivers of the peninsula have been proposed to be considered as wild and scenic rivers. If this occurs, they will receive some measure of protection against further habitat degradation. As part of a new ecosystems management approach, the U.S. Forest Service also is working with the U.S. Fish and Wildlife Service to improve watersheds on forest lands.

MAINTAINING OLD-GROWTH ECOSYSTEMS

The lowland forests now are mere shadows of their former selves. Old-growth spruce/hemlock forests once covered more than a million acres of the peninsula. About three percent of this ecosystem remains. More of the ancient forests in the Douglas fir/hemlock zone are intact, although much of the peninsula's old growth has been cut.

Harvesting rates have been so high in the last few decades that

Marymere Falls, tributary of Barnes Creek near Lake Crescent.

trees could not be regrown fast enough to replace those cut. Some areas could not be replanted successfully. Many logging families who worked the woods for generations now depend on the remaining old growth, mainly on National Forest Service land, to tide them over until second- and third-growth trees become large enough to harvest.

Olympic is one of the few national park areas that protects commercially valuable forest. John Muir once said, "There are trees in heaven that are safe from politicians and fire but there are none here." Historically, the boundaries of the former Olympic National Monument and the National Park were redrawn several times to exclude or protect large tracts of timber. But even within the national park, the forests have not always been safe from the saw. In the 1940s and the 1950s over 100 million board feet were cut inside the park, mainly under the supervision of a superintendent with a background in logging. Some of this was removed for legitimate reasons, but most was not. Today, individual hazard trees in the park may be cut down for safety in developed areas, but the logs are nearly always left to decompose near the site where they grew.

Large tracts of old growth are needed for long-term survival of spotted owls and the marbled murrelet. Great horned owls and the barred owl, a close relative of the spotted owl, thrive in cut-over forest lands. The barred owl's territory spread as the old growth fell, and these birds now compete for similar resources. Some of them also interbreed, contributing to the spotted owls' predicament.

Between six and seven hundred thousand acres of old growth remain on the peninsula, nearly all within Olympic National Park and Olympic National Forest. Smaller sections are managed by the Washington State Department of Natural Resources. Under debate now is how much land needs to be set aside to preserve these species and the old-growth forest as an intact ecosystem. Research completed so far indicates that the 350,000 to 400,000 acres of old growth within Olympic National Park are probably not enough to sustain spotted owl populations in the long run. A large "Designated Conservation Area" for owls has been drawn, which includes lands from Olympic National

Park and Olympic National Forest. Dozens of species of plants and animals that are potentially in danger would be protected in these conservation areas.

Different land management agencies on the peninsula often have conflicting mandates for administering their forests. Nearly all of them are required by various laws, not just the Endangered Species Act, to manage resources in a way that will ensure biological diversity and the preservation of individual species.

One potential solution is to change current logging practices on the peninsula from clearcutting to alternative harvesting methods. The Olympic Experimental Forest and Natural Resource Center were recently established on the west side of the peninsula to study ways of managing forests to produce timber and maintain ecological values. Clearcutting is the most economical method for removing trees, but it also impacts the land in many ways. Great amounts of topsoil wash off the hillsides into streams where it may smother salmon eggs buried in the gravel.

Clearcuts initially create more browse for deer and elk, but as the canopy closes over after about twenty-five years, available forage declines dramatically. This may be one of the main reasons elk populations seriously declined in the southeast corner of the peninsula. The fragmented forest, along with excessive trapping and poisoning, may also be responsible for the near disappearance of the fisher on the peninsula. This large member of the weasel family needs vast expanses of forest canopy, where it hunts squirrels and martens.

Visitors who drive the Highway 101 loop around the Olympics often complain

Above: Hemlock needles and Orego grape leaves.

———— ✳ ————

Facing page: Wat in a still side-chann of the Elwha River slowly travels towa the river's mouth a the Strait of Juan d Fuca.

about the clearcuts, which are generally much smaller today than they were in the earlier part of the twentieth century. Many people's reaction to clearcuts seems to go past reasoning and strike at their hearts. But the forest and the timber industry are an integral part of our lives. Most of us live in wooden homes and this book is printed on the tissue of former trees. If you live west of the Cascades, chances are good that your house now occupies the space where a massive conifer once stood.

Timber companies also are required to replant clearcuts within a few years of harvest, and it is often hard to see the young trees growing until they are a few feet tall. They essentially mature into tree farms that bear little resemblance structurally to natural forests. Wildfires and windfall leave many trees and snags standing, along with fallen logs that add to the future nutrient base of the new forest.

The Olympic Natural Resource center and experimental forest will look at different techniques known as "new" forestry that attempt to create more natural forest conditions. Many of these practices are labor-intensive and could provide more jobs for those in the industry. Changing forest management practices will cost money and increase the cost of lumber. Money also needs to be spent to help timber-dependent communities adapt and diversify.

The forestry and fishery issues facing the peninsula and the Pacific Northwest are incredibly complex, but solutions are possible for those who are willing to sit down and work together on the issues. Industry needs timberland set aside, which they know they can manage on a sustainable basis. All of us need intact natural forests that

ensure clean air and water, preserve diverse gene pools and provide places of recreation and renewal. The current battle over how these forests should be managed is only the latest in a war that has lasted a hundred years. May it be the last.

"…when the last individual of a race of living things breathes no more, another heaven and another earth must pass before such a one can be again."

—W. Beebe

Above: The Humptulips proposed wild and scenic river flows toward the Pacific Ocean in Olympic
National Forest.

———— ✳ ————

Facing page: Spotted owl, indicator species of a healthy old-growth forest ecosystem. Photo
copyright by Scott Price.

Above: *Autumn colors of big-leaf maple grace the shoreline of Lake Crescent.*

———— ✳ ————

Facing page: *The Pacific madrona grows along Hood Canal and in drier areas along the northeast Olympic Peninsula.*

Above: *Small mushroom on nurselog. Such logs can harbor more life when they are on the forest floor than they did when alive and standing as trees.*

———— ✳ ————

Facing page: *Fog condensing on conifer needles can significantly increase the amount of moisture available to the trees.*

Above: *Rhododendron, the state flower of Washington, displays springs blossoms on Mt. Walker, Olympic National Forest.*

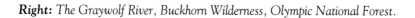

＊

Right: *The Graywolf River, Buckhorn Wilderness, Olympic National Forest.*

Above: *The coho salmon, also known as silver salmon, usually enter Olympic Peninsula rivers between August and November. Spawning traditionally occurs between September and December.*

———— ✳ ————

Facing page: *Water continues to erode and shape the landscape at Dosewallips Falls, Olympic National Park.*

Above: *Colonnade formed along a nurselog in the Quinault Rain Forest, Olympic National Park.*

———— ✳ ————

Facing page: *Mt. Skokomish Wilderness, one of the five areas dedicated as wilderness in the Olympic National Forest.*

Above: *The Sol Duc River, an important habitat for Coho salmon and steelhead, Olympic National Forest.*

———— ✳ ————

Facing page: *A leaf from big-leaf maple locked in ice in the greater Olympic ecosystem lowlands.*

I had just climbed to the top of Hurricane Hill and was taking in the glorious view.

Memories of a past climb in the Olympics reached across the decades…

The fog was so thick we couldn't see our feet. Sounds swirled up with mists from the forest—several hundred feet below. Here on the near-vertical rock face, life was reduced to a few patches of lichens. We were clinging to rock "pillows" formed 40 or 50 million years ago on the seafloor. But now, at the bottom of an ocean of air, the rock's secure footholds helped us inch our way to the top.

Things had changed since then and I now view the mountains and rock from a slightly different perspective. An eighty-foot fall from a tree forced me to slow down and see the world from a wheelchair. I still climb in my own way, but have learned that much joy can come from simply sitting and enjoying the world around us. The mountains are no less awesome—a blue grouse and I watch the sun set into the ocean.

"The stone grows old.
Eternity is not for stones.
But I shall go down from this airy space…
…and time will close about me,
and my soul will stir to the rhythm of the daily round.
Yet, having known, life will not press so close
and always I shall feel time ravel thin about me."
—*Eunice Tietjens*

THE HIGH COUNTRY

---　✳　---

Mountains dominate the heart of the peninsula. Like waves on the sea, the tangled peaks radiate in all directions. The Olympics are one of the youngest and fastest growing mountain ranges in the world. Geologists debate the exact cause of uplift, but agree the movement of the earth's massive crustal plates is ultimately responsible. As the North American continent overrode the ocean floor, an enormous pile of accumulated sediments and basalts was wedged into the corner of the existing continent. Intense pressures crumpled and folded the rock and stood the sedimentary layers on end.

Today, the ocean floor continues to dive under the North American plate, but there is evidence part of it may be "hung up." Laser measurements show the entire Olympic range is compressing from east to west. The coastal side of the peninsula is rising, while Hood Canal is sinking. Many geologists feel these changes foretell the possibility of a massive earthquake. If the pressure from the snagged portion of the two plates releases suddenly, an 8- or 9-point quake (at the top end of the Richter scale) could occur. Geologic evidence reveals that similar earthquakes occur in this area every several hundred years. A quake of this size could produce immense *tsunami* waves in the ocean and would profoundly affect the peninsula's human communities.

Alpine glaciers are responsible for the Olympic's rugged appearance more than any other factor. Water originally eroded the land into rolling hills, then glaciers gnawed and carved the ridges into an intricate sea of peaks. Over 60 glaciers exist today, most of which were formed during a cooler period about 2,500 years ago. They are tiny compared to their former size, but they are still forces of geologic change.

These glaciers alternately swept down mountain valleys and retreated back many times in the past. During interglacial periods, alpine glaciers melted back much faster than the immense continental glaciers that filled Hood Canal and the Strait of Juan de Fuca. Runoff down some of the valleys was blocked by the larger glaciers, forming ancient high valley lakes.

CLOUD FORESTS

As you climb the slopes, forests become cooler and species begin to change. Mountain clouds drift through the trees while Douglas squirrels fight over cones. This is the montane zone. Conifer species from both the higher and the lower zones can be found here, but silver fir tends to dominate on the west side of the park. Silver fir's dark green needles and silvery bark emphasize its alternate name, lovely fir. Early travelers felt the tree's boughs made the best bedding, a poor idea today. Even the smallest branches have needles running along them, helping the silver fir absorb light in the forest's depths.

On the drier northeast corner of the peninsula, silver fir grows only in isolated colder areas. Douglas fir cloaks the mountain sides. Wisps of yellow-green and gray lichens with colorful names like old-man's beard and wolf lichen hang off branches and grow along the moist sides of trunks. These lichens are good indicators of the ever-present clouds.

Avalanche tracks slice through the trees from above. Different types of vegetation growing in the tracks indicate avalanche frequency—resilient slide alders are most abundant. These bushy chutes provide easy access to the high country for some lowland birds.

IN THE SUBALPINE

The subalpine zone is a magical place where steeple-shaped conifers rule and deep snow covers the ground much of the year. The smell of legions of wildflowers in open meadows can be overpowering at times. Here, forests give up their last hold on the land.

The upper limits of the subalpine are marked by snow, wind and fire. Lower limits vary widely in the Olympics from east to west and are strongly influenced by moisture and snow depth. Mountain hemlock and subalpine fir are the two main conifer species, while Alaska yellow cedars and lodgepole pine are less common. Cedars are the oldest-growing trees in the Northwest—some biologists believe the cedars can live for 3,500 years.

Subalpine trees have either short or flexible branches that shed snow more easily than those of lowland species. Longer, stiffer branches would quickly snap off in winter storms. Branches buried in snow for several months are sometimes attacked by snow mold, a black slimy fungus jokingly referred to as "bear wipe." The mold does not appear to cause too much damage to the trees. Lichens grow abundantly here; the

Winter view toward the Bailey Range from Hurricane Ridge.

Above: *High-country summer range for the black bear.*

———— ✳ ————

Facing page: *Columbia blacktail deer frequent subalpine meadows. Many of the deer that live within the national park are accustomed to humans.*

lowest tufts of old-man's beard on the trees generally mark the level of the highest snowpacks.

The balance between subalpine forests and meadows is very complex, but conifers generally invade wetter meadows during warmer years when snows melt earlier and growing seasons are longer. If the ground is too dry, however, seedlings cannot establish themselves. Some trees grow "skirts" beneath them—a ring of new seedlings and branches from the parent trees that may layer and develop roots of their own. Fire played an important role in forming many of the subalpine meadows in the Olympics. One lightning storm in a long summer drought can start dozens of small fires, and many trees at this elevation burn like sparklers.

On Hurricane Ridge, subalpine meadows are the favorite haunt of the Colum-

bia black-tailed mule deer. These graceful animals are much more powerful than they look. Antlerless females have been known to kill attacking wolves with well-placed kicks of their sharp hooves. Park visitors tempted to feed deer place themselves and their families in danger and disrupt the animal's natural feeding habits.

Deer live in a world governed by scent. Glands located on their foreheads, legs and between their hooves produce pheremones that leave messages for other deer. These odors mark territory and trails, establish breeding readiness and warn others of danger. Deer follow the snow down the mountainside in winter.

Black bear frequently are also seen feeding in subalpine meadows. Their tastes are very eclectic and range from ants to carrion, although most of their meals are vegetarian. Backpackers should be sure to hang their food and keep their campsites clean to keep bears wild. Slimy bear scat is often a sign that the animals have been rooting through the ground in search of truffles. In other areas of Washington, black bears come in an assortment of browns, but bears on the peninsula are exclusively black. The Olympic short-tailed weasel and the snowshoe hare also have distinct coloration. On the peninsula, these animals stay brown throughout the winter instead of turning white.

The Olympic marmot is genetically distinct from other marmots. These curious animals generally prefer to establish colonies in the bottoms of cirques and depressions in subalpine parklands. Here they have a wide variety of food. As the snow-line retreats up the mountainside, marmots follow, grazing on the fresh shoots of newly emerged plants. But plants on warmer, south-facing slopes tend to blossom all at once, creating a less than optimal habitat because of the short-term abundance of food. Each summer, two-year-old marmots are forced out of their colonies to fend for themselves, and often first move to these areas. Such sites are sometimes referred to as "marmot ghettoes."

In late summer, large hatches of band-wing grasshoppers attract several species of birds, including small owls, from the forests below. Blue grouse saunter through meadows, often oblivious to humans. Smaller birds pick a variety of insects from late-lying snowbanks.

Higher still, trees are reduced to ancient gnarled forms that create eerie shad-

Above: Olympic marmot, endemic species of the Olympic high country.

———————— ✳ ————————

Facing page: Pink mountain heather blossoms in Grand Valley, Olympic National Park.

ows when clouds roll in. Low juniper bushes and patches of heather dot the landscape. This *krummholz*, or "crooked wood," may be hundreds of years old, but only inches in diameter. During winter, any living branches above the snowpack are blasted by winds carrying ice crystals as hard as sand.

LAND ABOVE THE TREES

Meteorologists believe that the mountain air in the Olympics vies with Antarctica as the cleanest air in the world. Expansive mountain views contrast with the lilliputian plants that survive in the alpine zone. Winter winds sweep ridgetops bare, but small highly-adapted plants are able to survive. One strategy is to keep a low profile—wind speeds are much lower near the ground than they are a few inches above it. Some plants grow in cushions or mats that catch wind-borne bits of soil and seeds. These may have extensive root systems that store energy for the long winter.

Some of the rarest and most unique plants of the Olympics grow in the alpine. Piper's bellflower, Flett's violet and cut-leaf synthyris are among the eight plants that are endemic—only found on the Olympic Peninsula. Several other species are found in a larger range between Vancouver Island, Mt. Rainier and Saddle Mountain in Oregon, but nowhere else in the world.

Permanent snowbanks and glaciers have a life of their own. By summer's end, blooms of algae may be abundant—one species tends to concentrate airborne radioactive particles. Ice worms feed on the minute plants growing in the snow. Water

Cinquefoil brightens a dry alpine ridge on Grandview Peak.

Freezing temperatures in the high country can last from September through May.

pipits, rosy finches and migrating birds feed on a variety of insects and seeds that are blown up from the valleys below.

OF SPECIAL CONCERN

Subalpine and alpine plants share the remote reaches of the mountains with the mountain goat. The goats are descendents of twelve animals that were released near Lake Crescent in the 1920s. The animals were transplanted through the combined efforts of Washington State wildlife agents, the U.S. Forest Service and a local sportsmen's club. The purpose of the introduction is not clear, but providing hunters with a stock of animals was likely a primary consideration.

Sixty years later, the population had grown to roughly 1,175 animals, about a thousand of which were in Olympic National Park. When the earliest biological surveys were done in the mountains, mountain goats were not seen. There were a few anecdotal references to goats in the literature of the day, and some of the coastal tribes had items made from goats, but intertribal trade between the peninsula and British Columbia was common. After reviewing all available evidence, biologists concluded that the peninsula's isolation had kept mountain goats from becoming established in the Olympics, along with many other species of mammals, birds and plants. Mountain goats are common, however, in British Columbia and the Cascades.

The National Park Service views the animals as "exotic" to Olympic National

Above: Mt. Olympus, 7,965 feet high, is the tallest feature on the Olympic Peninsula. It has an active alpine glacial system.

———— ✳ ————

Facing page: A small falls at the outlet of PJ Lake in Olympic National Park.

Park. As part of their mandate to preserve natural ecosystems and processes, parks are directed to manage populations of exotic plant and animal species, up to and including eradication, whenever such species threaten park resources. Extensive research over the last decade showed that goats caused significant changes in fragile mountain plant communities, including those with rare and endemic wildflowers.

To limit the damage, the park service experimented with a number of live-capture and sterilization techniques. Some goats were given "field vasectomies" and over 400 goats were captured and transported to other areas in the Northwest where they would become hunting stock. The capture operation, costing roughly $1,000 per goat, finally ended when the helicopter operations that were being used were declared too dangerous. Wildlife sterilization experts also met and concluded that no methods currently existed that could be used to conclusively control the free-ranging goat population. Forty-seven goats died as part of this overall program. Twenty-eight died from stress or injury during the capture process, and the other nineteen were killed for biological purposes. A multi-agency environmental impact statement is underway that is reviewing options for managing mountain goats on the Olympic Peninsula.

Goats are not the only species that have been introduced to the peninsula. In addition to commonly known animals (like pigeons, starlings and Norway rats), quail, pheasants, red fox, bull frogs and largemouth bass have been brought in. Over 250 species of plants are also exotic. Most are relatively benign, but some like reed canary grass, Canadian thistle and holly aggressively invade new territory.

Wildfires burned naturally across the peninsula for tens of thousands of years. Our modern suppression efforts have saved millions of dollars worth of timber in commercial areas, but fire played an integral part in the evolution of our current ecosystem. Olympic National Park had a natural fire management plan in place before the Yellowstone National Park fires occurred in 1988. All fires are now being suppressed while the plan is being rewritten. The new plan will call for continued suppression of human-caused fires, while using prescribed natural fire to manage and restore remote mountain habitat.

Backpackers also create a number of changes in the high country. Disease control specialists estimate that 10 to 20 percent of the total population in the U.S. carry the backpacker's scourge, giardia. The percentage in dogs may be much higher. This intestinal parasite has made many people unhappy they didn't treat the water before they drank it. Proper disposal of human waste, away from water, is paramount.

People cause one of the biggest impacts to mountain vegetation with their own two feet. In popular high-country areas, some habitats are very sensitive to trampling, especially low shrubby vegetation and ridgetop alpine cushion plant communities. In these areas, damage that occurs over a one- to two-year period can take 50 to 100 years to regenerate. In some places, the damage may be irreparable. The park service is revegetating some denuded campsites and networks of social trails with plants grown in park greenhouses.

Permit restrictions in both Forest Service and Park Service wilderness on the peninsula help reduce damage. Both agencies are developing wilderness management plans that identify and help limit how much change humans bring to the backcountry. Wilderness itself is a resource we will value more and more as the world shrinks around us.

TOWARDS THE FUTURE

In a biological sense, the Olympic Peninsula truly is an island. From mastodon hunters to backpackers, its remarkable diversity has attracted humans for thousands of years. This rich puzzle of species and habitats has great ecological, economic, recreational and spiritual value for all of us.

A multitude of public agencies manage this resource, sometimes with conflicting mandates. But in the end, the fate of one species often hinges on that of the next. And we are not left out of this cycle. The discovery that the scraggly yew tree produces a cancer-fighting drug is one example. Well-managed forests have the potential to provide

Mt. Duckabush and an alpine tarn, headwaters of the east side of Duckabush River.

economic benefit, bolster salmon runs and preserve wildlife populations. We can choose instead, however, to "mine" natural resources without regard to what we leave for our children.

Olympic National Park is recognized throughout the world community as both an International Biosphere Reserve and a World Heritage Site. Humans have changed so much of the earth in so little time. There are few places left we can go to see how things were before "civilization" arrived. As our population grows and time passes, these natural areas will become increasingly important.

Much larger issues than those we have discussed so far have the potential to impact the Olympic Peninsula in far-reaching ways. The possibility of global climate change is one. Researchers are studying treeline levels in the national park to gather baseline information. This can be used in the future to compare warming, or cooling, trends. At this point, we do not know how global warming, the ozone hole, or our exponentially increasing world population will affect these ecosystems or ourselves. What we do know is that we are conducting a grand experiment—our grandchildren will "discover" the results.

Learning to manage the peninsula as a single ecosystem is a challenging task. More research is needed. Increased cooperation and partnerships among city, county, tribal, state and federal governments are mandatory. Wise use and good long-range strategic planning are paramount. What do we want this area to look like in 100 years? In 500 years? One Native American tribe believed they should make decisions based on not only how they affect the present generation, but also how they affect the next seven generations.

There are many things each of us can do in our daily lives to help. Not all are easy, but we need to start somewhere. The choice is ours.

"We travel together, passengers on a little spaceship dependent on its vulnerable supplies of air and soil: all committed for our safety to its security and peace, preserved from annihilation only by the care, the work, and I will say the love we give our fragile craft."

—Adlai Stevenson

Above: *Wind pattern on high-country snowpack that lingers into the summer months, creating a very short growing season for many alpine plants.*

———— ✳ ————

Facing page: *The high winds of winter at Hurricane Ridge create sinuous snow patterns.*

Above: *Many species of lichen encrust a rock outcrop on Blue Mountain. These lichens gradually erode the rock and help create soil.*

————— ✳ —————

Left: *Autumn color of dwarf huckleberry in Cameron Basin.*

Above: *The Flett violet is a rare endemic species found only in the high country of the northeastern Olympic National Park.*

———— ✳ ————

Facing page: *Dense groupings of lupine give a blue hue to the summer subalpine meadow at Hurricane Ridge.*

Above: *Winter winds sculpt subalpine trees into masterpieces of snow and ice.*

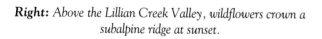

Right: *Above the Lillian Creek Valley, wildflowers crown a subalpine ridge at sunset.*

FOR FURTHER READING

———— ✱ ————

GENERAL

Bergland, Eric O., and Jerry Marr, *Prehistoric Life of the Olympic Peninsula*. Seattle: Northwest Interpretive Association, 1988.

Harris, Ann G., and Esther Tuttle, *Geology of National Parks*. Dubuque, Iowa: Kendall/Hunt Publishing Company.

Kozloff, Eugene N., *Plants and Animals of the Pacific Northwest*. Seattle: University of Washington Press, 1976.

Kruckeberg, Arthur R., *The Natural History of Puget Sound Country*. Seattle: University of Washington Press, 1991.

O'Hara, Pat, and Tim McNulty, *Olympic National Park: Where the Mountain Meets the Sea*. Del Mar, California: Woodlands Press & Northwest Interpretive Association.

Sharpe, Fred, *Olympic Wildlife Checklist*. Seattle: Northwest Interpretive Association, 1992.

Tabor, Roland W., *Geology of Olympic National Park*. Seattle: Northwest Interpretive Association, 1987.

Warren, Henry C., *Olympic: The Story Behind the Scenery*. Las Vegas, Nevada: KC Publications, Inc., 1982.

THE COAST

Angell, Tony, and Kenneth C. Balcomb III, *Marine Birds and Mammals of Puget Sound*. Seattle: University of Washington Press, 1982.

Howorth, Peter C., *Whales—Dolphins—Porpoises of the Pacific*. Las Vegas, Nevada, KC Publications, Inc.

Kolb, James A., and Diane Boardman, *Puget Soundbook*. Poulsbo, Washington: Marine Science Center of the Pacific Northwest, 1991.

Love, John A., *Sea Otters*. Golden, Colorado: Fulcrum Publishing, 1992.

Snively, Gloria, *Exploring the Seashore in British Columbia, Washington and Oregon*. Seattle: Gordon Soules Book Publishers, Ltd., 1978.

Steelquist, Robert U., *Washington's Coast*. Helena, Montana: American Geographic Publishing, 19487.

Wortheim, Anne, *The Intertidal Wilderness*. San Francisco: Sierra Club Books, 1994.

THE FORESTS

Arno, Stephen F., *Northwest Trees*. Seattle: The Mountaineers, 1977.

Buckingham, Nelsa M., and Edward L. Tisch. *Vascular Plants of the Olympic Peninsula, Washington*. Seattle: University of Washington/National Park Service Cooperative Park Studies Unit, UW/CPSU Report B-79-2, 1979.

Ervin, Keith, *Fragile Majesty: The Battle for North America's Last Great Forest*. Seattle: The Mountaineers, 1989

Franklin, Jerry F., and C.T. Dyrness, *Natural Vegetation of Oregon and Washington*. Portland: USDA Forest Service General Technical Report PNW-8, 1973.

Harper, Alice B., *The Banana Slug*. Aptos, California: Bay Leaves Press, 1988.

Henderson, Jan A., et al., *Forested Plant Associations of the Olympic National Forest*. Portland, Oregon: USDA Forest Service R6 ECOL Technical Paper 001-88, 1989.

Kirk, Ruth, with Jerry F. Franklin, *The Olympic Rain Forest: An Ecological Web*. Los Angeles: University of Washington Press by Perpetua Press, 1992.

Lien, Carston, *Olympic Battleground*. San Francisco: Sierra Club, 1991.

Norse, Elliot A. *Ancient Forests of the Pacific Northwest*. Washington, D.C.: Island Press/The Wilderness Society, 1990.

Steelquist, Robert U., *Field Guide to the Pacific Salmon*. Seattle: Sasquatch Books, 1992.

Vitt, Dale H., et al. *Mosses, Lichens & Ferns of Northwest North America*. Seattle: University of Washington Press, 1988.

THE HIGH COUNTRY

Arno, Stephen F., and Ramona P. Hammerly, *Timberline: Mountain and Arctic Forest Frontiers*. Seattle: The Mountaineers, 1984.

Harris, Stephen L., *Agents of Chaos: Earthquakes, Volcanoes, and Other Natural Disasters*. Missoula, Montana: Mountain Press Publishing, 1990.

Mathews, Daniel, *Cascade–Olympic Natural History*. Portland, Oregon: Raven Editions with Portland Audubon Society, 1988.

Steelquist, Robert U. *Washington Mountain Ranges*. Helena, Montana: American Geographic Publishing, 1986.

Stewart, Charles, *Wildflowers of the Olympics and Cascades*. Port Angeles, Washington: Nature Education Enterprises, 1988.

Pat O'Hara has lived on and photographed the Olympic Peninsula for over a decade. Although his busy assignment schedule frequently takes him traveling throughout North America and abroad, he always dedicates a substantial portion of time each year to photographing in his home territory. Working full time as a freelancer since 1978, Pat has gained an international reputation as an environmental photographer. His credits include fourteen large-format books showcasing his work, hundreds of magazines and calendars, as well as national advertisements. He is currently working on a long-term photography project about the Beringian Heritage International Park, proposed by the United States and Russia. Photo by Tina Smith-O'Hara.

Michael Smithson has worked as a ranger naturalist for the National Park Service for fifteen years. He has spent many years climbing in the Olympic Mountains and exploring the peninsula. After earning a degree in wildlife biology from the Evergreen State College, Michael completed additional studies at the University of Washington and the University of Colorado. He has written other books on the natural history of the Rocky Mountains, and lives with his wife and two children on the Olympic Peninsula.